Easy Harmo Songbook

with Online Audio Access

By
Connor Rand

For 10 Hole "C" Diatonic Harmonica

For Free Online Audio Access
Go to this address on the internet:

cvls.com/extras/ehs

About This Book

This is a collection of fifteen popular harmonica tunes that can be played on a "C" harmonica. All of these songs were chosen because they can be easily performed by players of any level. Most of the playing is in the middle of the harmonica's range, from the 3rd to the 8th hole, because this is the part of the harmonica that is the most playable and, with some practice, anyone can make these notes sound good. Also, with one exception at the very end of the book, none of the songs require any bends, which can be difficult for beginners.

Audio Tracks

There are online Audio Tracks available for each of these songs. As you listen to the sample recordings you may notice some subtle bending and various forms of vibrato; these are stylistic performance choices that an individual player would make, and are not essential to the melody of the song, and are therefore not included in the notation.

You may access these files by going to the following web address:

cvls.com/extras/ehs

The Author

Connor Rand is a multi-Instrumentalist (harmonica, guitar, banjo) who grew up in Atlanta, GA. He has played in a variety of bands, taught music lessons, and is a graduate of the University of Georgia. For the past twenty years, Connor has worked as a professional musician. He is now a resident of Nashville, TN where he performs live music and is a songwriter and collaborator.

Table Of Contents

Section 1
Getting Started

We are including the Getting Started Section from the *Harmonica Primer* course in case you need to brush up on your technique. If you find some of these songs and techniques too difficult, this is a great refresher course and is available on Amazon.com.

Parts of the Harmonica

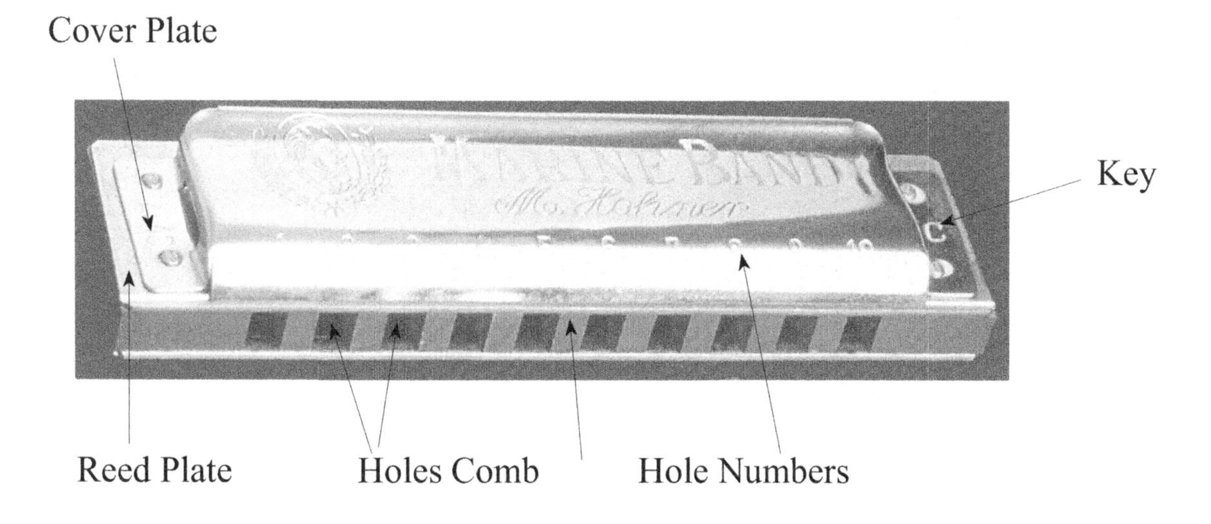

Selecting & Caring for Your Harmonica

We will be using a 10 hole diatonic harmonica in the key of C. (The key is stamped on the top of each harmonica). If you have a different harmonica, you can save it to play in different keys later. Unfortunately, state health laws prohibit the return of harmonicas because they are placed on your mouth. If you have any questions regarding choosing your harmonica, your local music store can help.

There are two basic rules in caring for your harmonica:

1. Always play with a clean, dry mouth.

2. When you finish playing the harmonica, tap it out several times to remove any moisture from the reeds.

This is virtually all you need to do to maintain your harmonica (harp for short). Running water through a harp is a risky venture. Although you may unstick an old reed, too much water will make the wood swell, which could hurt your lips. Taking care of your harmonica will make it last a long time.

Harmonica Notation

The 10 holes in the harmonica play one note when you blow and another when you draw. Here are the notes played when you blow and draw.

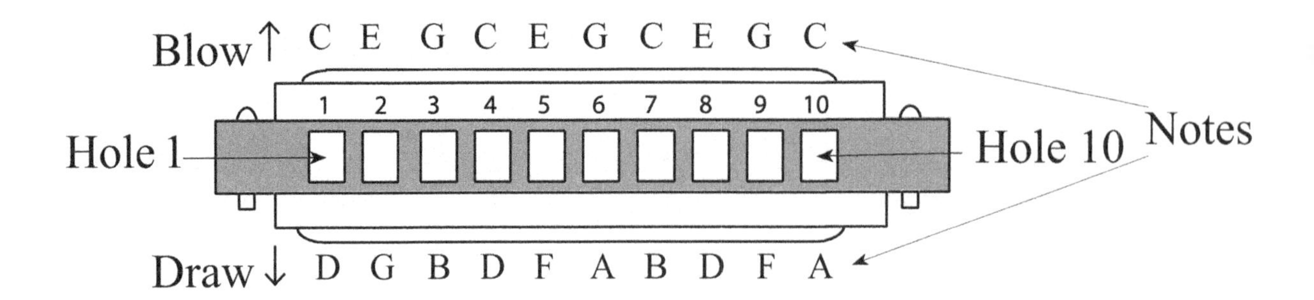

We will be using a number and arrow system to show you when to blow or draw through the harmonica. An up arrow means to blow, think "blowup". A down arrow means to draw air or inhale through the harmonica.

The numbers we use represent the holes in the harmonica. There are 10 possible holes to play through starting numerically from left to right. Hole number 1 is on the far left of the harmonica if the holes are facing you. Hole number 10 is on the far right of the harmonica.

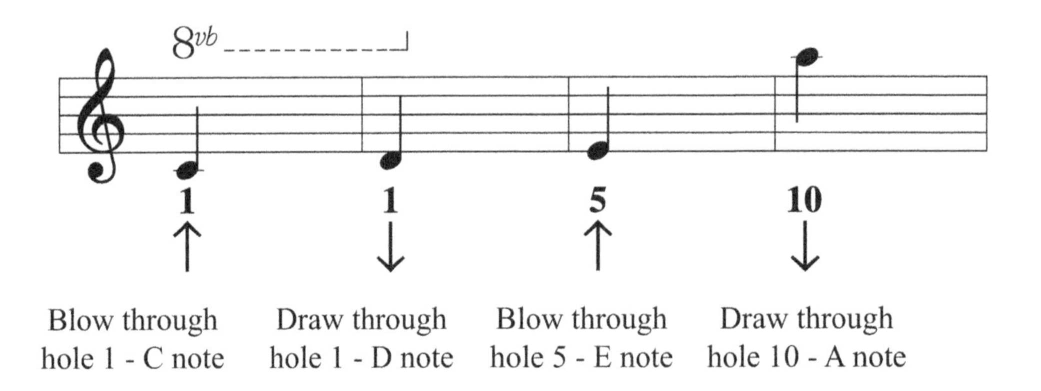

Blow through hole 1 - C note

Draw through hole 1 - D note

Blow through hole 5 - E note

Draw through hole 10 - A note

Music Notation

A whole note gets 4 beats.

A half note gets 2 beats.

A quarter note gets 1 beat.

An eighth note gets half a beat.

The Staff

The staff consists of 5 lines and 4 spaces. Each line and space represents a note.

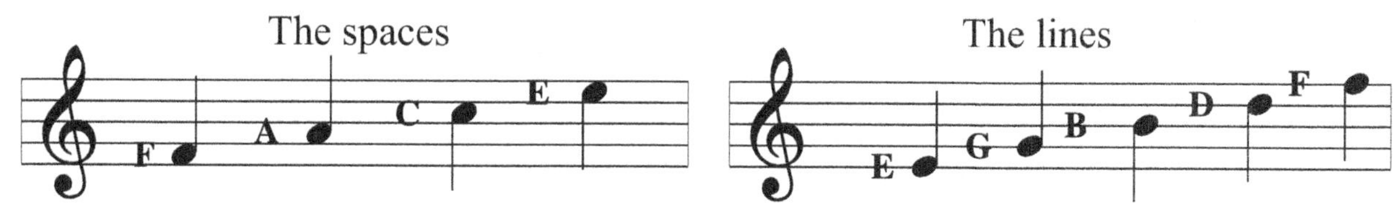

The spaces spell the word: F A C E

The lines may be remembered by:
Every **G**ood **B**oy **D**oes **F**ine

Ledger Lines

Ledger lines allow us to write notes above or below the staff.

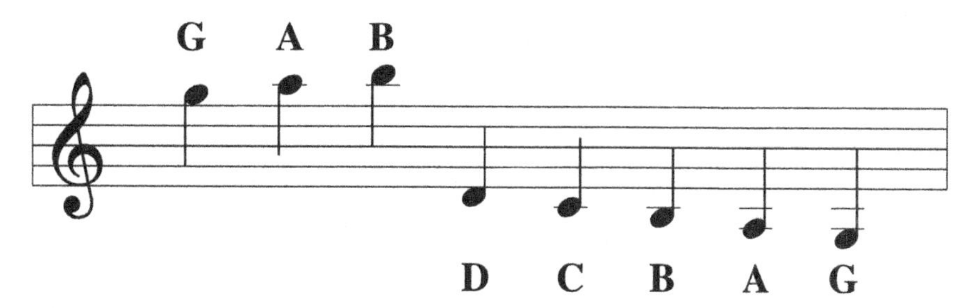

The Clef, Measures, & Barlines

Harmonica music generally uses the treble clef. The staff is divided into measures by barlines.

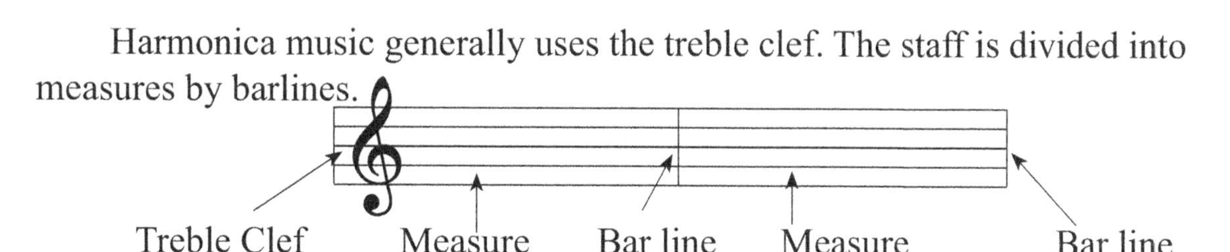

Rests

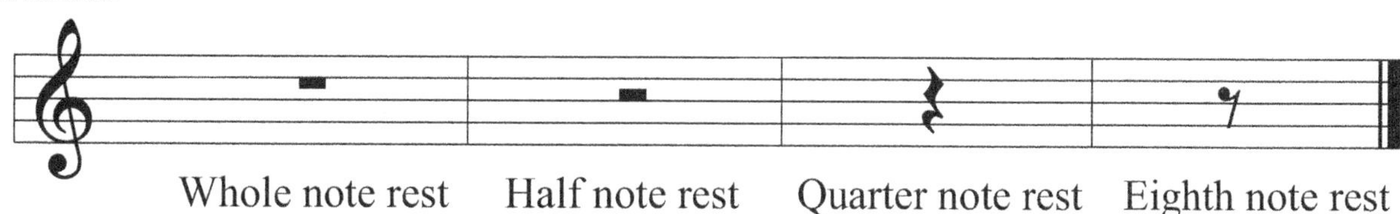

Time Signatures

The time signature tells you how many beats are in a measure and what note gets one beat.

In 4/4 time or common time, there are 4 beats in a measure and the quarter note gets one beat.

In 3/4 time there are 3 beats in a measure and the quarter note gets one beat.

In 6/8 time there are 6 eighth notes in a measure and the eighth note gets one beat.

Dots & Ties

A dot adds half the value of the note it's added to. A dotted quarter note lasts 1 1/2 beats.

A tie connects two notes across a bar line. A half note tied to a quarter gets 3 beats.

8vb

This means the actual notes are played 1 octave lower. Using this allows us to use fewer ledger lines and makes note reading easier.

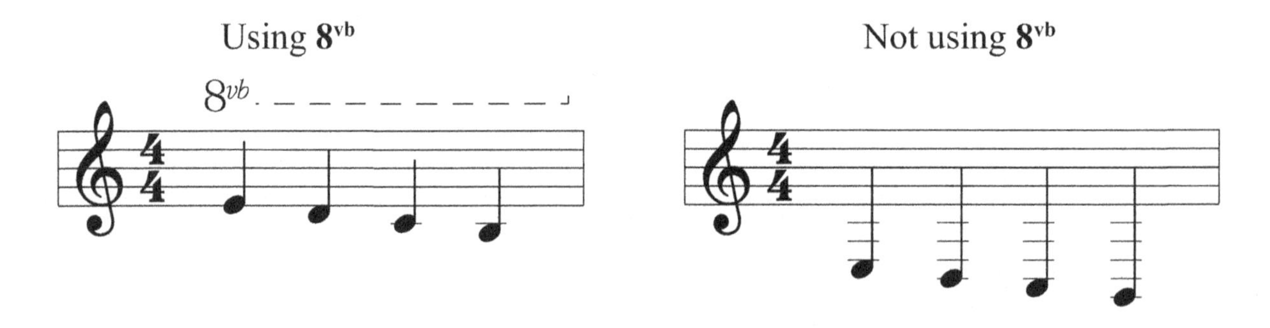

Holding the Harmonica

There are several accepted ways to hold the harmonica. This is what I recommend.

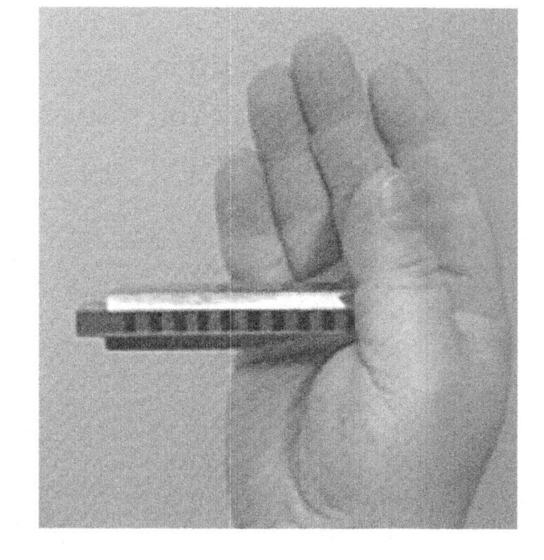

Step 1

With the holes facing you numbered 1 to 10 going from left to right, cup your right hand around the harmonica.

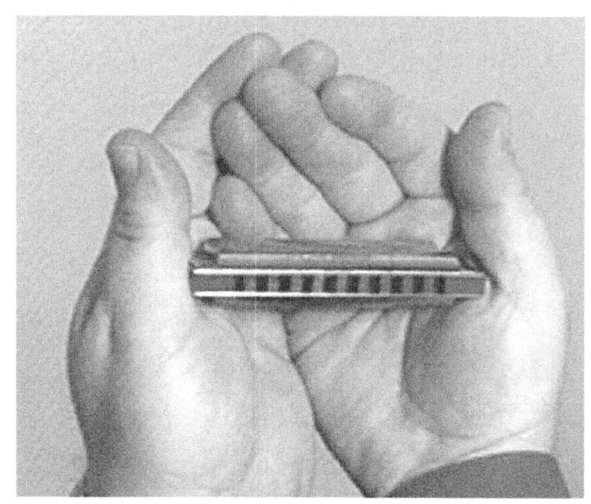

Step 2

Let the left side of the harmonica rest against your left hand with the fingers cupped around the harmonica.

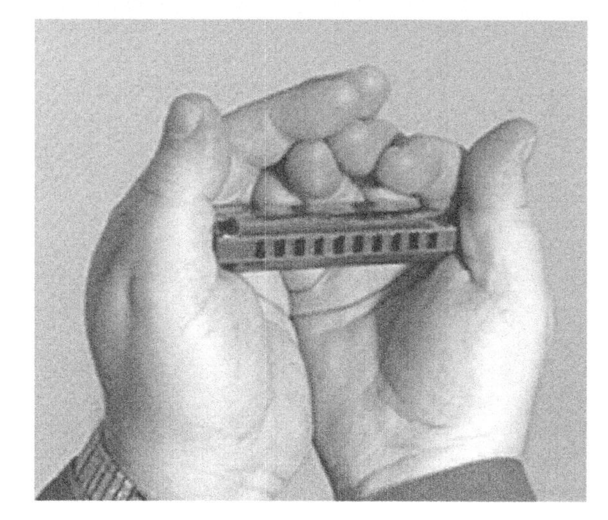

Step 3

Do not block any of the holes with any part of your hand and don't squeeze the harmonica.

Blowing

Step 1

Hold the harmonica like we have just learned and bring the harmonica to your mouth and blow. You must shape your mouth around each hole creating a vacuum, not letting air through any place but the hole you are playing. Try to blow into one hole at a time.

Step 2

A good exercise is to take a straw, place it in your mouth, and blow through it. Feel how your mouth is shaped around the straw. That's what your mouth needs to do around each hole. Try sucking in through the straw. This is how air must pass through each hole in the harmonica.

Exercise 1

Place the harmonica to your mouth and blow through hole number 1. Remember 8vb means the note sounds 1 octave lower than written.

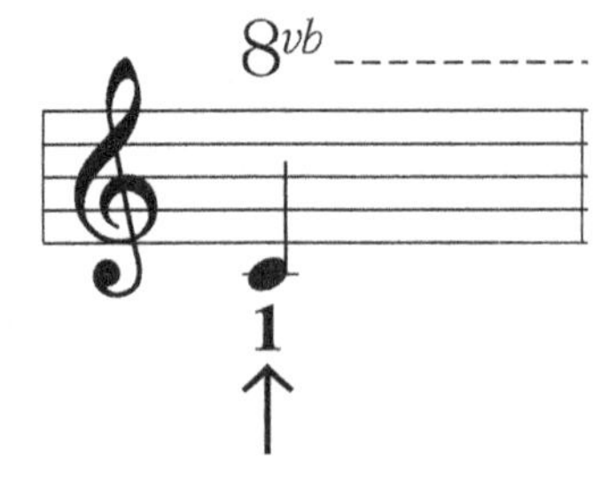

Try to play just one note. A good way to practice this is to place the tip of your tongue against the hole you are playing. Shape your lips around your tongue, withdraw your tongue, (keeping this shape with your mouth) and blow into the hole. This should give you one note. We don't use this technique when playing. This is just to help you get the feel of playing one note at a time.

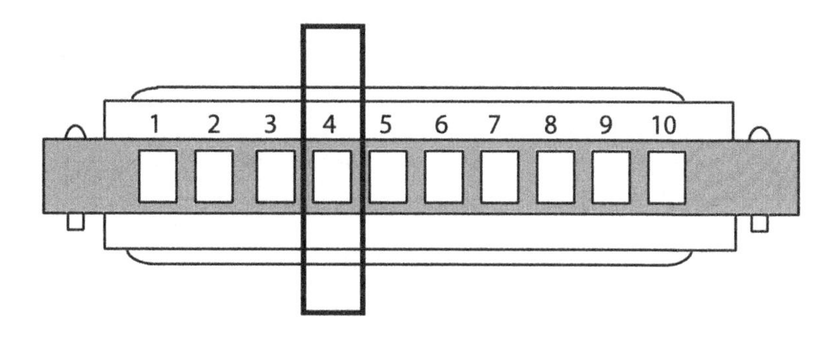

Exercise 2

Practice blowing through each hole of the harmonica. Remember 8vb means the notes are played one octave lower than written.

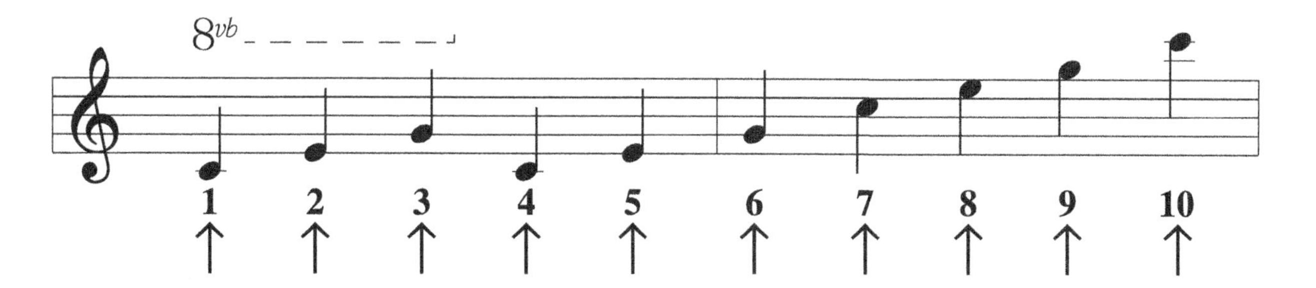

Here is another way to practice playing one note at a time. Place your thumbs over the holes on both sides of the hole you intend to play, blocking those holes. Now place your mouth up to the harmonica, positioning it over the hole you intend to play. Now remove your fingers and play. Practice playing one note at a time until you can play it smoothly.

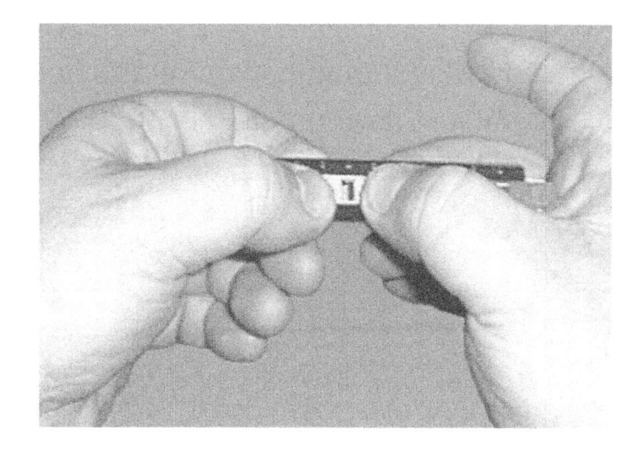

Drawing

Exercise 3

Draw or inhale through each hole.

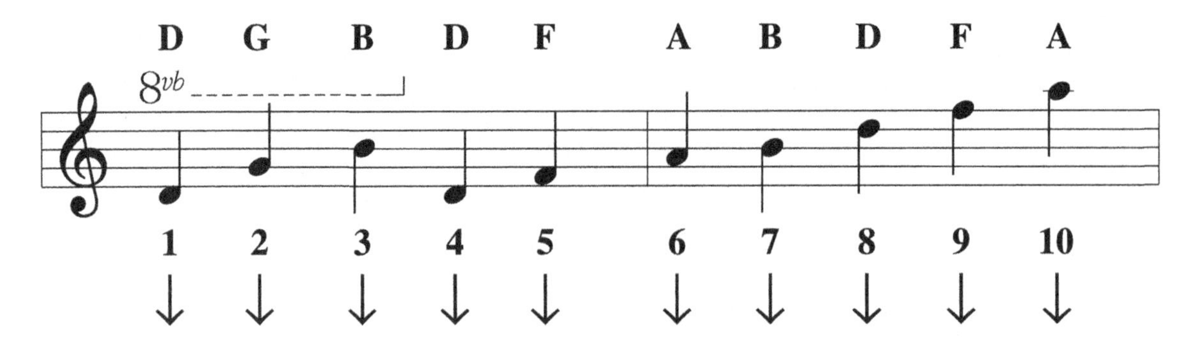

Exercise 4

Blow through holes 1 through 4, then draw through each hole coming backwards. Practice this until you can play each note without making more than one sound at a time.

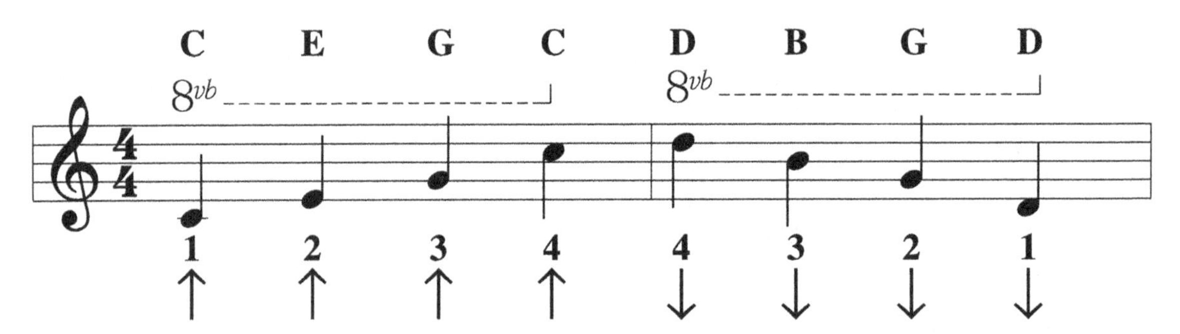

The C Major Scale

Exercise 5

We will now learn how to play a major scale on the harmonica. This is a C Major scale since we are using a C harmonica.

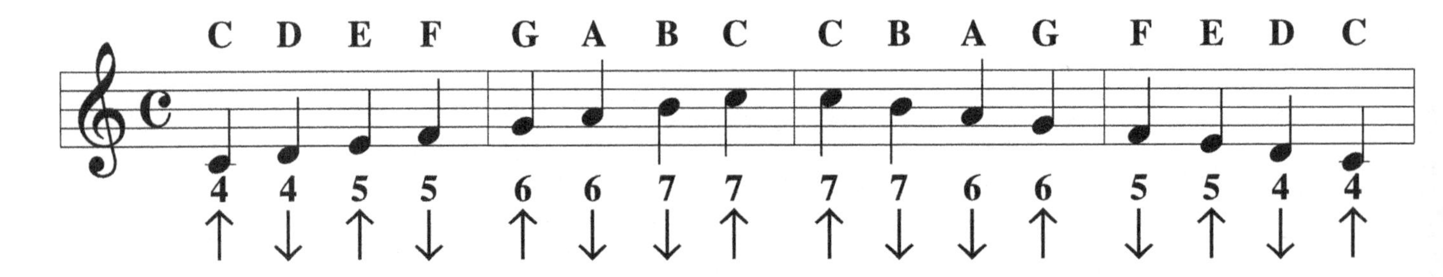

Section 2
The Songs

These songs are presented in order of easier to harder arrangements. Feel free to make the songs as simple or as complex as your playing level allows.

Online Audio Access is available at this address on the internet:

cvls.com/extras/ehs

Go Tell Aunt Rhody

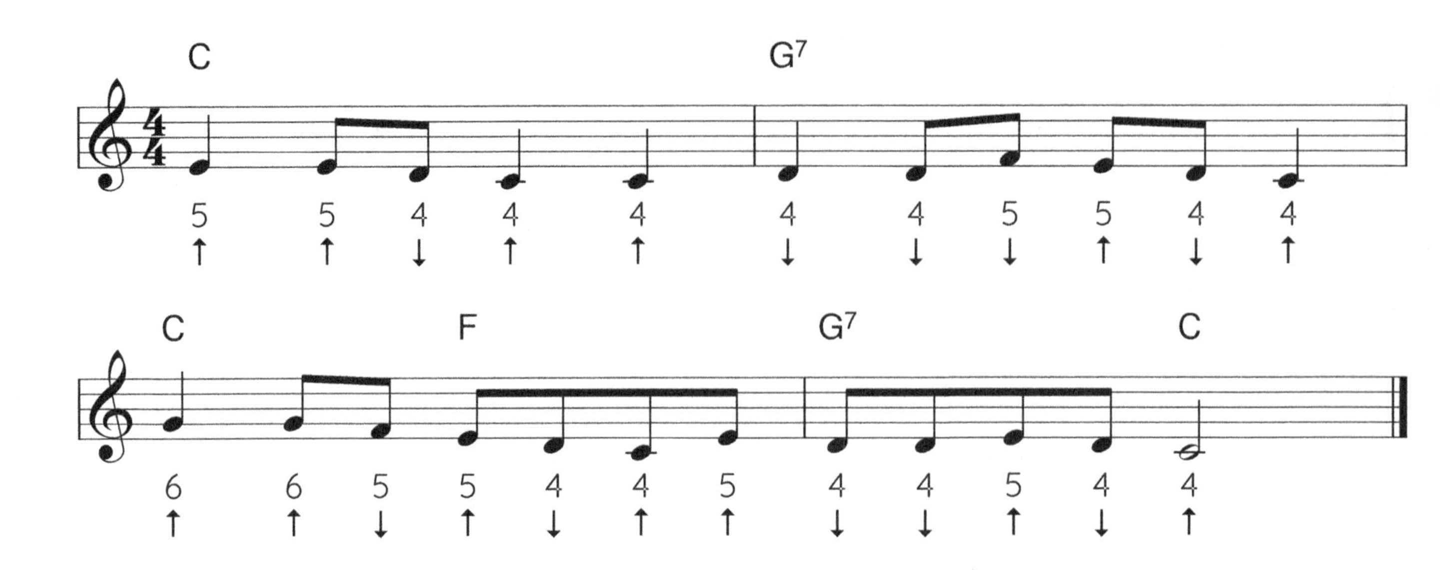

If you are a beginner, practice this song measure by measure. Memorize measure 1 before going on to measure 2. Make sure to play along with the audio tracks.

Note: The lyrics to all of these songs are available in Section 3, starting on page 31.

You Are My Sunshine

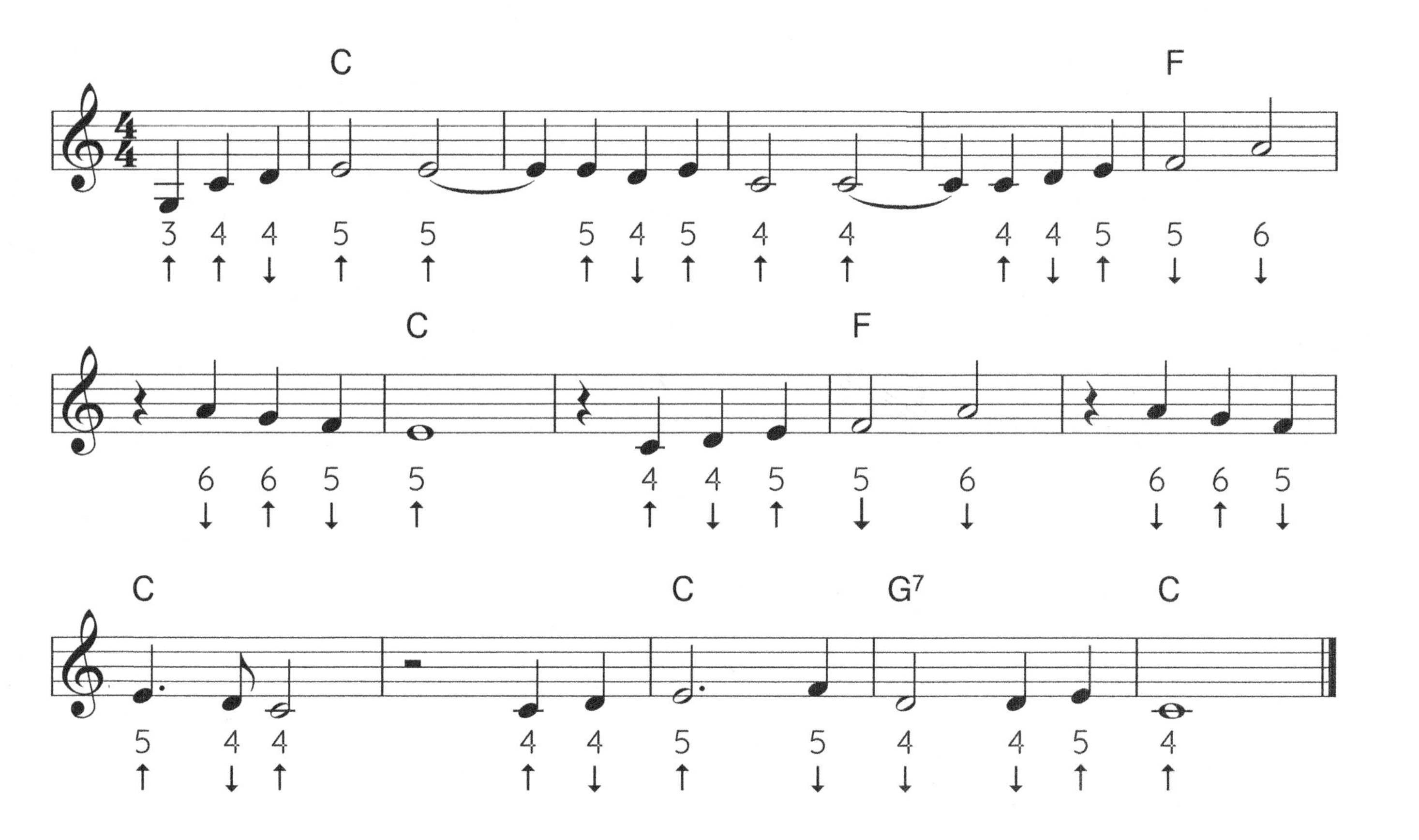

Home Sweet Home

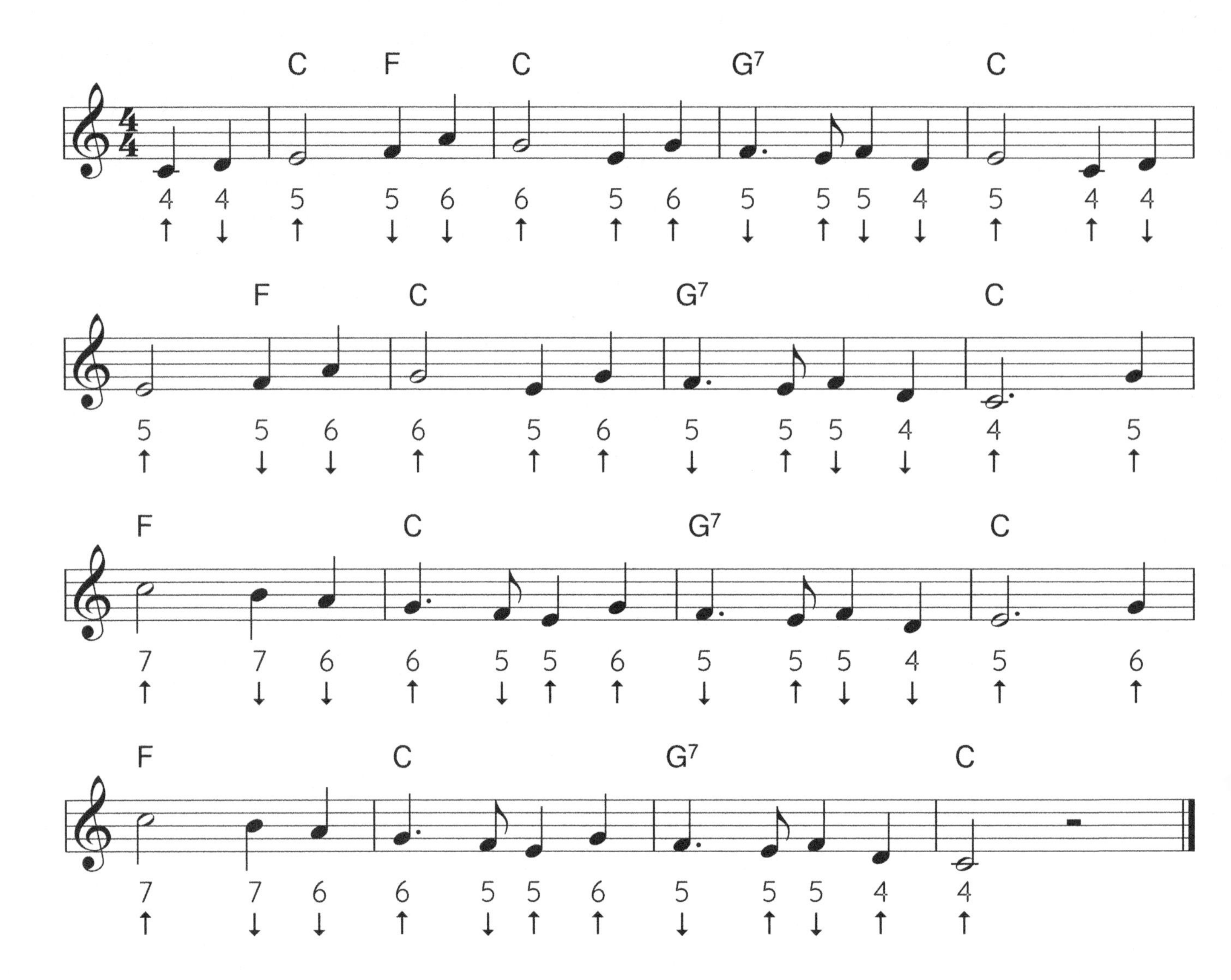

Home Sweet Home is commonly played as an instrumental and was made popular by Earl Scruggs on the banjo. This will not be included in Section 3 - Lyrics.

Bury Me Beneath the Willow

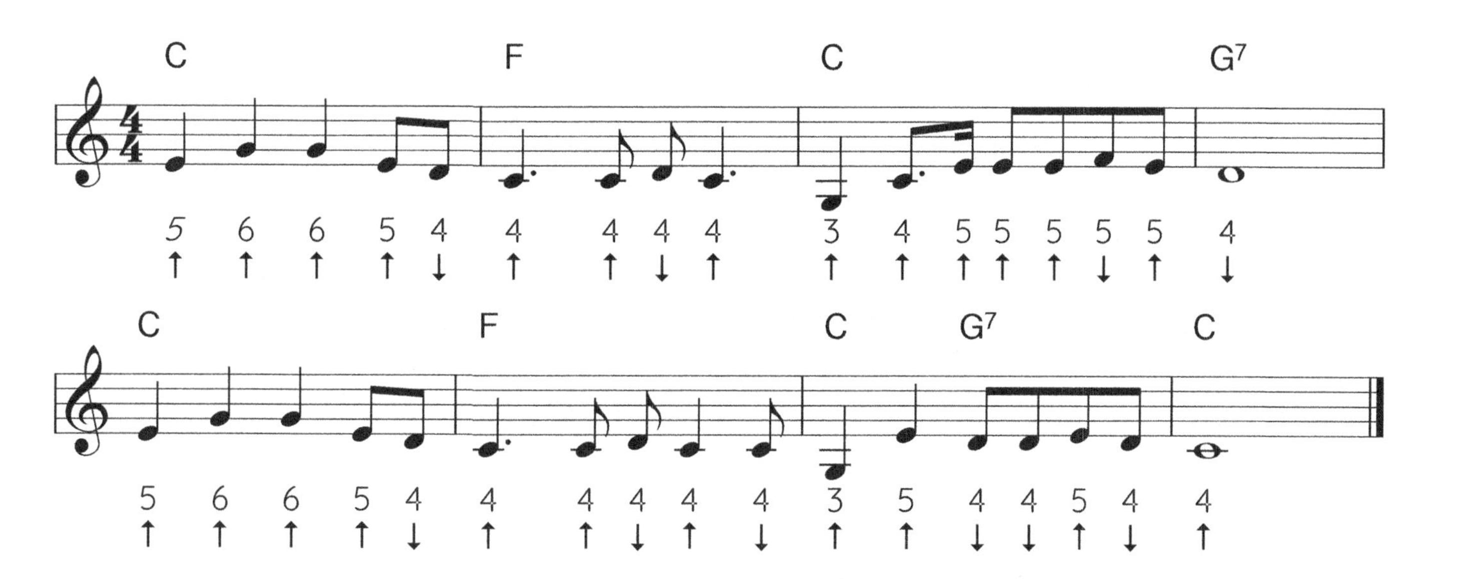

Irene, Goodnight

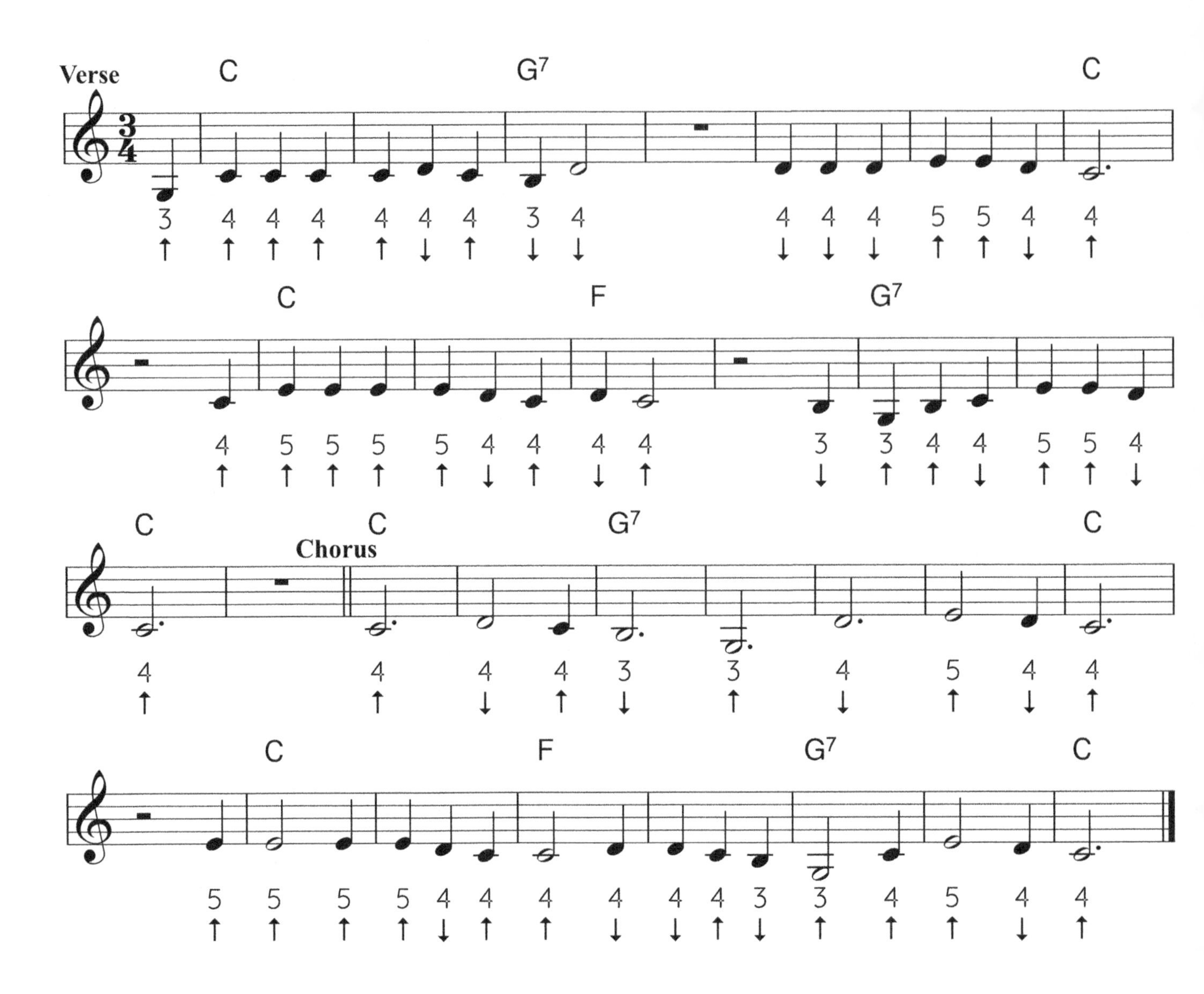

Goin' Down The Road Feelin' Bad

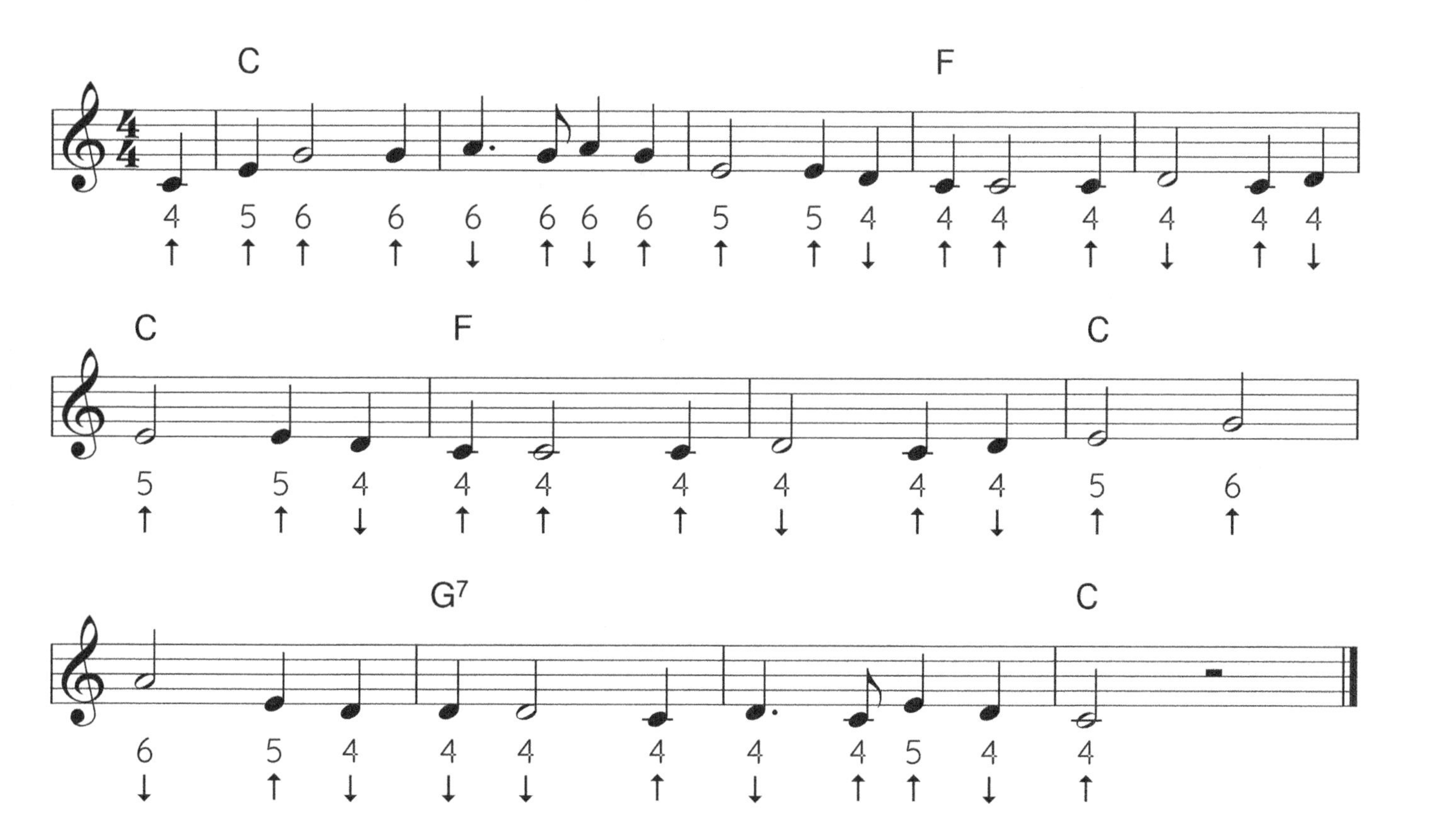

My Old Kentucky Home

Sweet Betsy From Pike

Simple Gifts

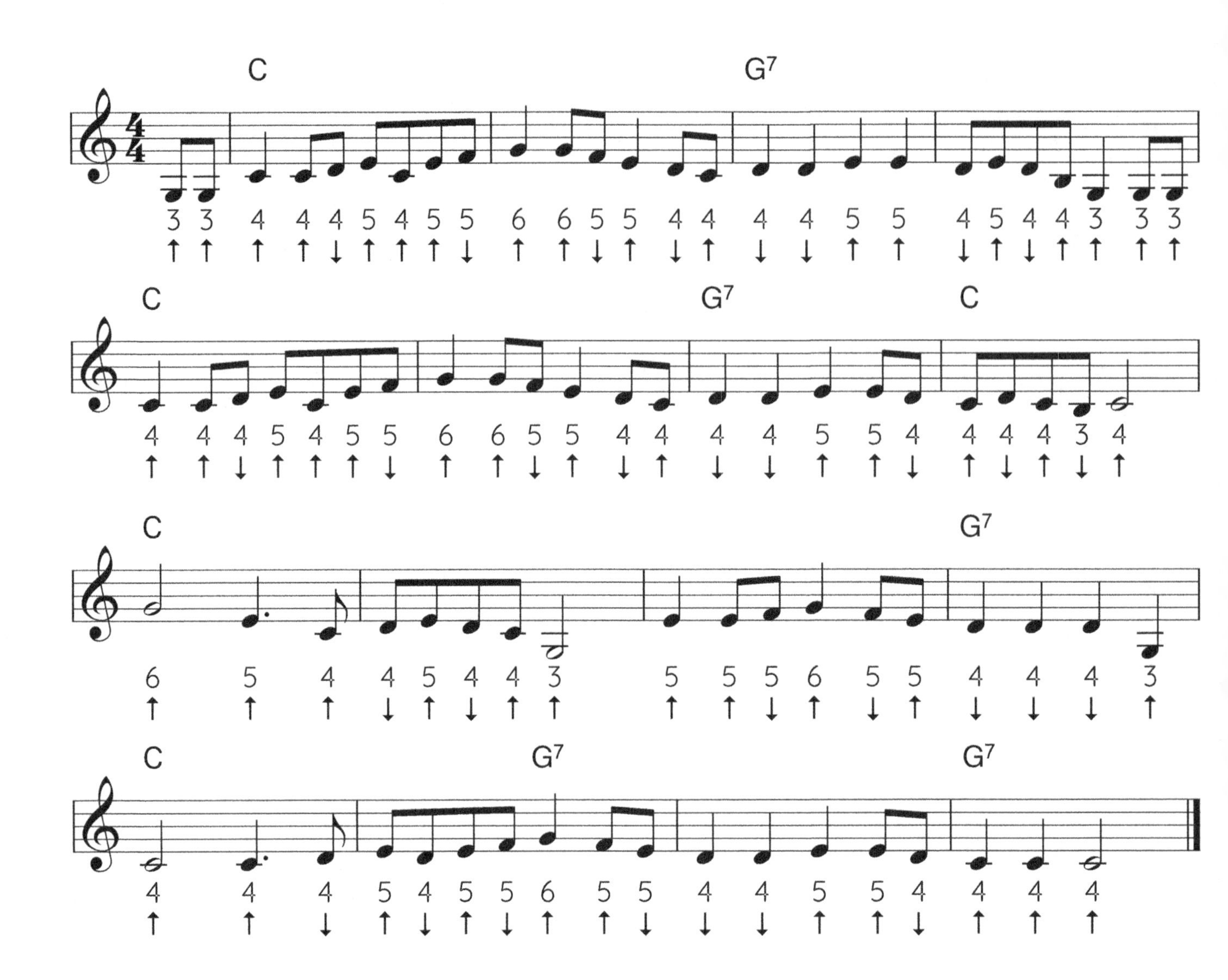

Shenandoah

C F
3 4 4 4 4 5 5 6 6 7 7 6 6 6 6
C F C
5 6 6 6 6 6 6 6 6 4 4 4
Am Em C G7 C
5 4 5 6 6 4 4 5 4 5 4 4 4

Wreck of the Old 97

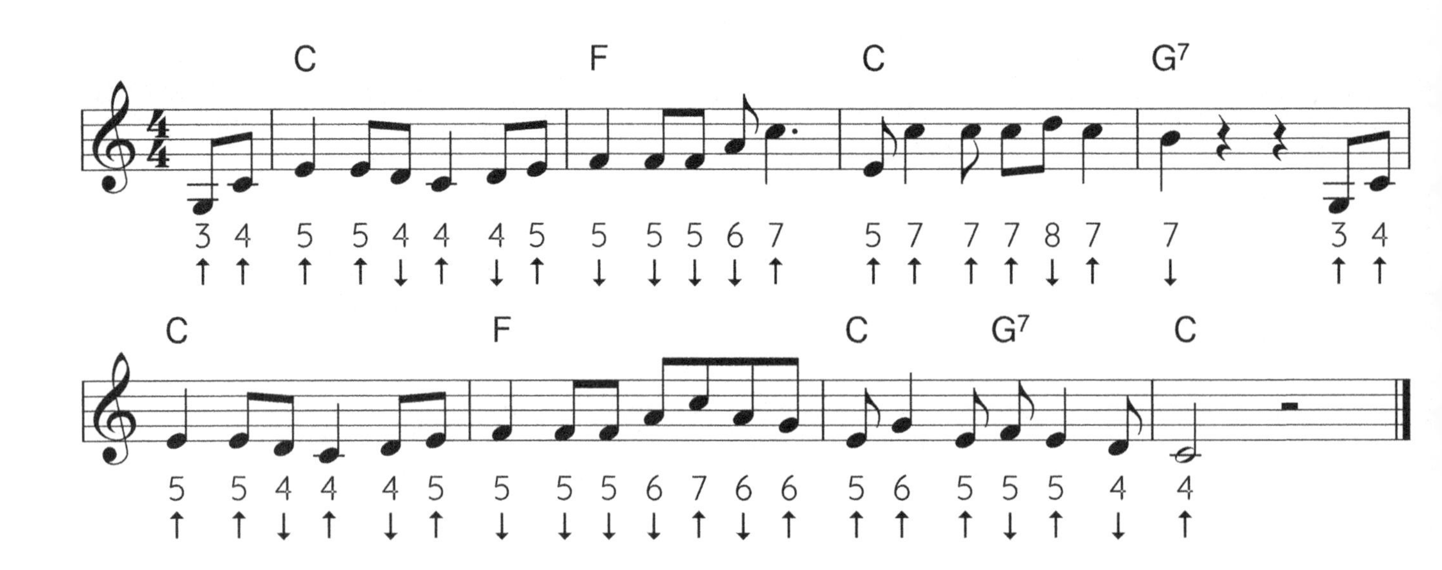

Old Folks at Home

Molly Malone

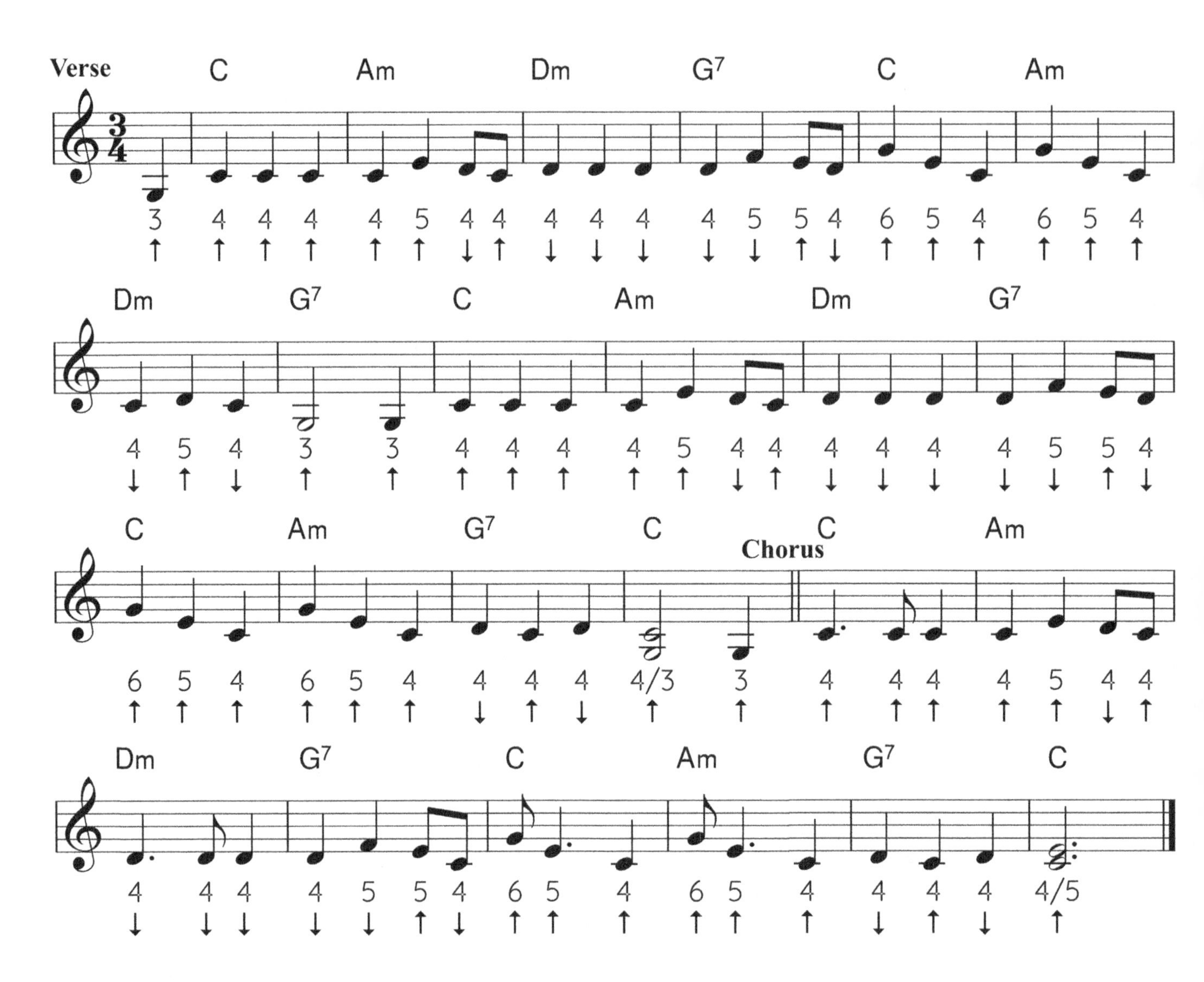

Double Stops

Playing two notes at a time is called a double stop. This happens quite naturally when first learning how to play. The trick is to control when you are playing more than one note at a time, and which ones you are playing. This occurs in the third and fourth lines of *Molly Malone*.

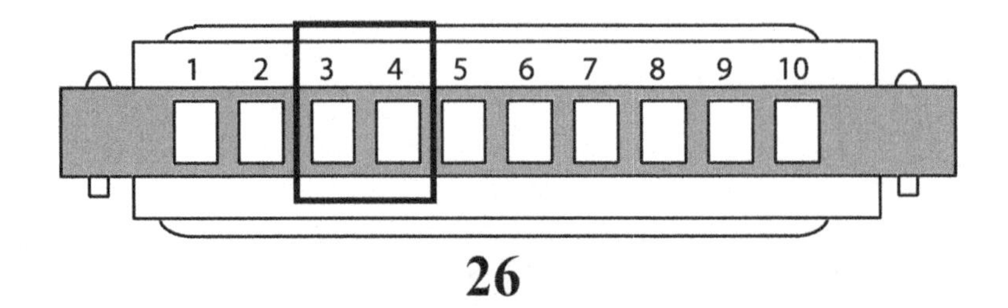

It Hurts Me Too

8vb means the actual melody is played one octave lower on the harmonica. This is used to make it easier to read the music notation by having fewer ledger lines. The holes and arrows are correct as written. See page 10.

Cross Harp

It Hurts Me Too is played in 2nd position or “Cross Harp”. Although we are using a C harmonica, we will actually play in the key of G. Harmonica players use this technique a great deal in order to solo or to play the blues. When you play cross harp, there are more inhale notes than exhale notes. This allows for many more expressive effects and techniques.

St. James Infirmary

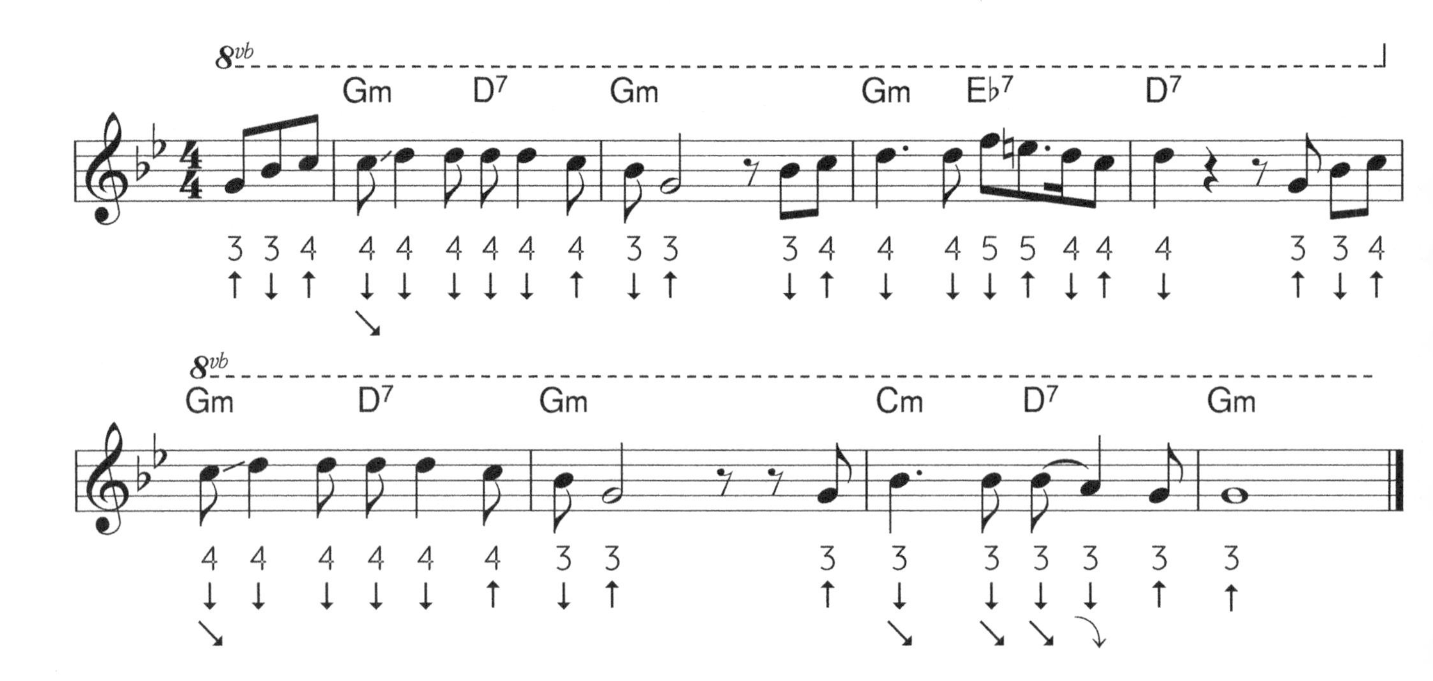

Bends

The angled arrow indicates a bend which is changing the pitch of a note by forcing more wind through the reed. This is commonly done by drawing or inhaling.

Hold your harmonica as usual. Tongue position becomes important here. Start with your tongue in the middle of your mouth. Draw air through hole 3 and make an "EEE Yew" shape with your mouth.

While making an "EEE Yew" motion, our tongue goes forward and down, and the jaw should also move forward. Remember to inhale the whole time you are making the "EEE Yew" shape. We are not actually making an "EEE Yew" sound, just the motion with our mouth and tongue. Beginners usually try to inhale too hard during this technique. Remember, finesse is required here, not force.

Note: *St. James Infirmary* has 2 flats in the key signature. We are playing cross-harp in the key of G minor.

We're also using 8vb again in this song. This means the actual melody is played one octave lower on the harmonica.

Section 3
Lyrics

This section contains the melody line, lyrics, and chord progressions so that you can play the complete version of the songs with all of the lyrics. This also works great for jam sessions or playing on stage because the lyrics are in a large font with the chord progression on each verse. This section is also arranged in alphabetical order to make finding the songs easier.

Bury Me Beneath the Willows

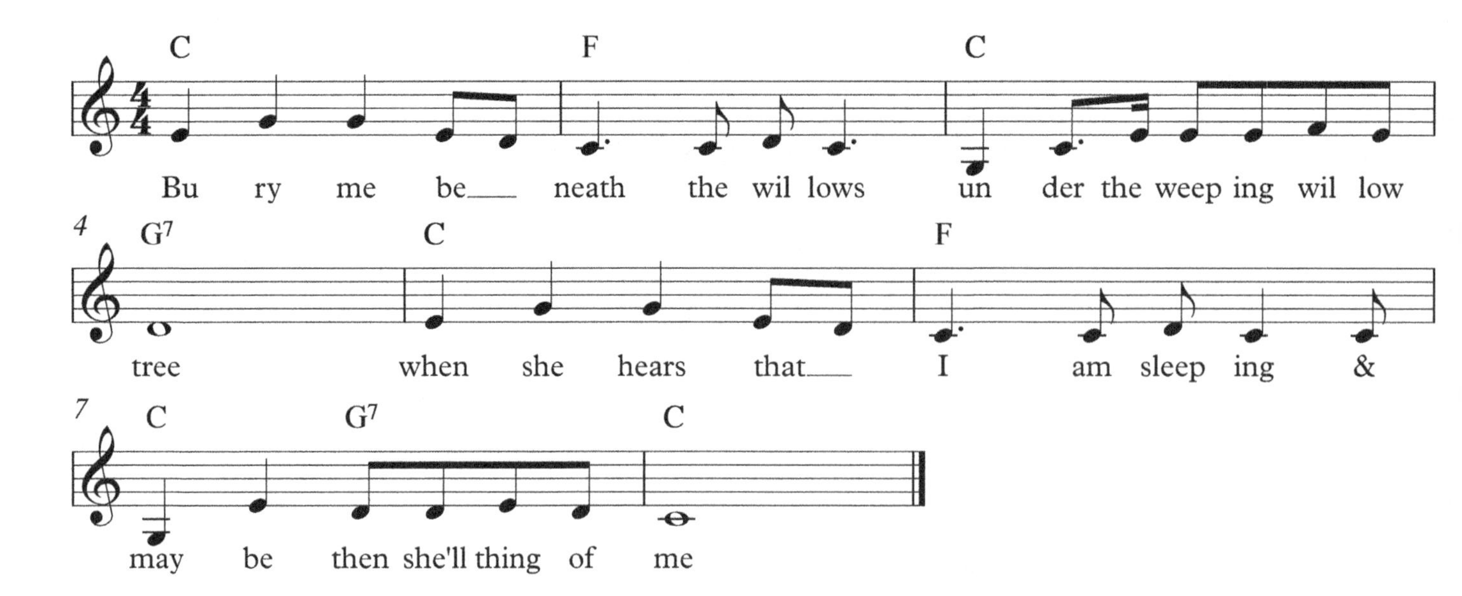

C F
My heart is sad and I'm in sorrow
C G7
Weeping for the one I love
C F
When shall I see her, oh, no never
C G7 C
Till we meet in Heaven above

C F
Tomorrow was to be our wedding
C G7
But Lord, oh Lord, where can she be?
C F
She's gone, she's gone to find another
C G7 C
She no longer cares for me

C F
She told me that she did not love me
C G7
I couldn't believe it was true
C F
Until an angel softly whispered,
C G7 C
"She no longer cares for you".

C F
Place on my grave a snow white lily
C G7
To prove my love for her was true
C F
To show the world I died of grieving
C G7 C
For her love I could not win

Go Tell Aunt Rhody

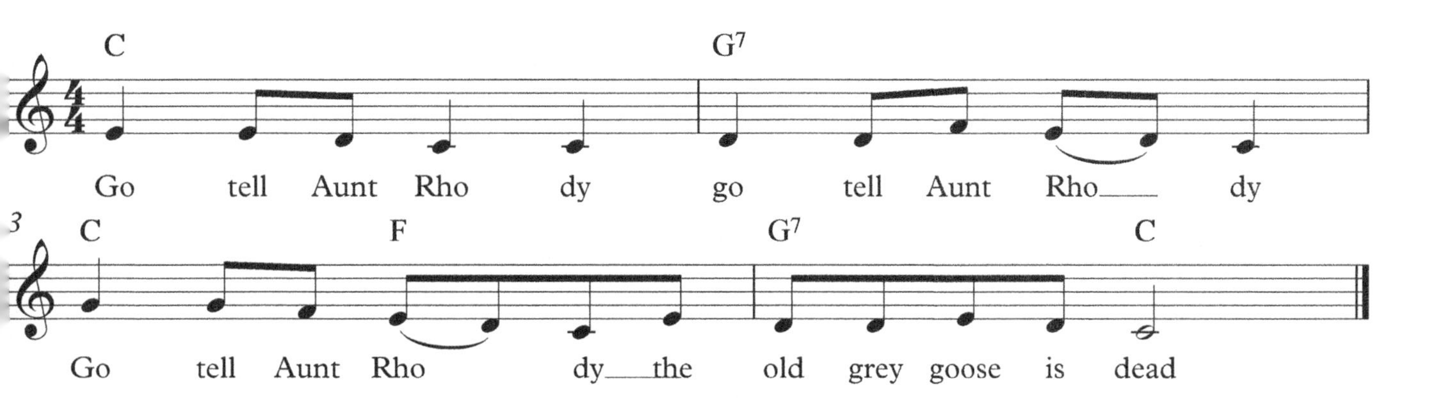

C
The one she's been saving
G7
The one she's been saving
C F
The one she's been saving
G7 C
To make a feather bed

C
The old gander's weeping
G7
The old gander's weeping
C F
The old gander's weeping
G7 C
Because his wife is dead

C
The goslings are mourning
G7
The goslings are mourning
C F
The goslings are mourning
G7 C
Because their mother's dead

C
She died in the mill pond
G7
She died in the mill pond
C F
She died in the mill pond
G7 C
From standing on her head.

Goin' Down That Road Feelin' Bad

Got me [C]way down in jail on my knees
This [F]jailer, he sure is hard to [C]please
[F]Feed me on corn bread and [C]peas, Lord, Lord
And I [G7]ain't gonna be treated this a [C]way

Sweet [C]mama won't buy me no shoes
She's [F]left with these lonesome jail [C]house blues
My sweet [F]Mama won't buy me no [C]shoes, Lord, Lord
And I [G7]ain't gonna be treated this a [C]way

These [C]two dollar shoes they hurt my feet
The [F]jailer won't give me enough to [C]eat
These [F]two dollar shoes they hurt my [C]feet, Lord, Lord
And I [G7]ain't gonna be treated this a [C]way

I'm [C]going where the climate suits my clothes
I'm [F]going where these chilly winds don't [C]blow
I'm [F]going where the climate suits my [C]clothes, Lord, Lord
And I [G7]ain't gonna be treated this a [C]way

Irene, Goodnight

C G7
Sometimes I live in the country
C
Sometimes I live in the town
F
Sometimes I have a great notion
G7 C
To jump into the river and drown
Chorus

C G7
Stop rambling, and stop your gambling
C
Stop staying out late at night
F
Go home to your wife and your family
G7 C
Sit down by the fireside bright
Chorus

It Hurts Me Too

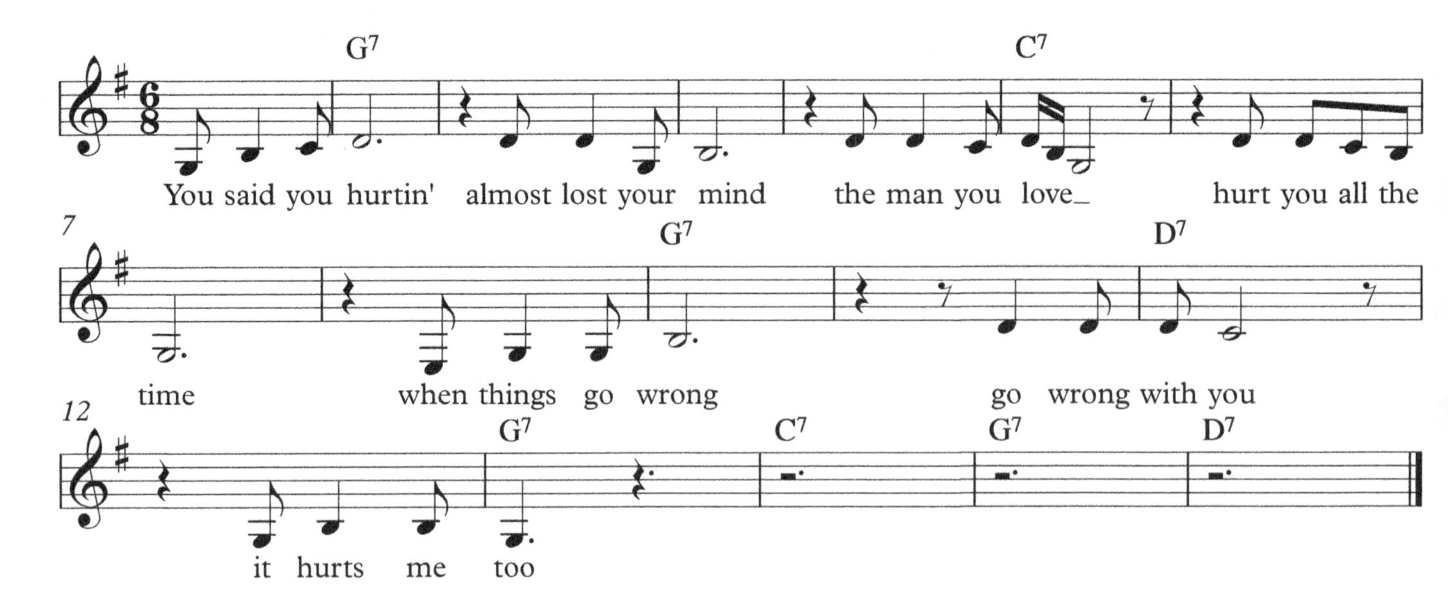

You said you hurtin', you almost lost your mind (G7)
The man you love he hurt you all the time (C7)
When things go wrong, go wrong with you (G7 … D7)
It hurtin' me too (G7 C7 G7 D7)

You love him more, when you should love him less (G7)
Why pick up behind him and take his mess (C7)
But when things go wrong, go wrong with you (G7 … D7)
It hurtin' me too (G7 C7 G7 D7)

He loves another woman, and I love you (G7)
But you love him and stick to him like glue (C7)
When things go wrong, go wrong with you (G7 … D7)
It hurtin' me too (G7 C7 G7 D7)

He'd better leave you, or you better put him down (G7)
Because I won't stand to see you pushed around (C7)
But when things go wrong, go wrong with you (G7 … D7)
It hurtin' me, too (G7 C7 G7 D7)

Molly Malone

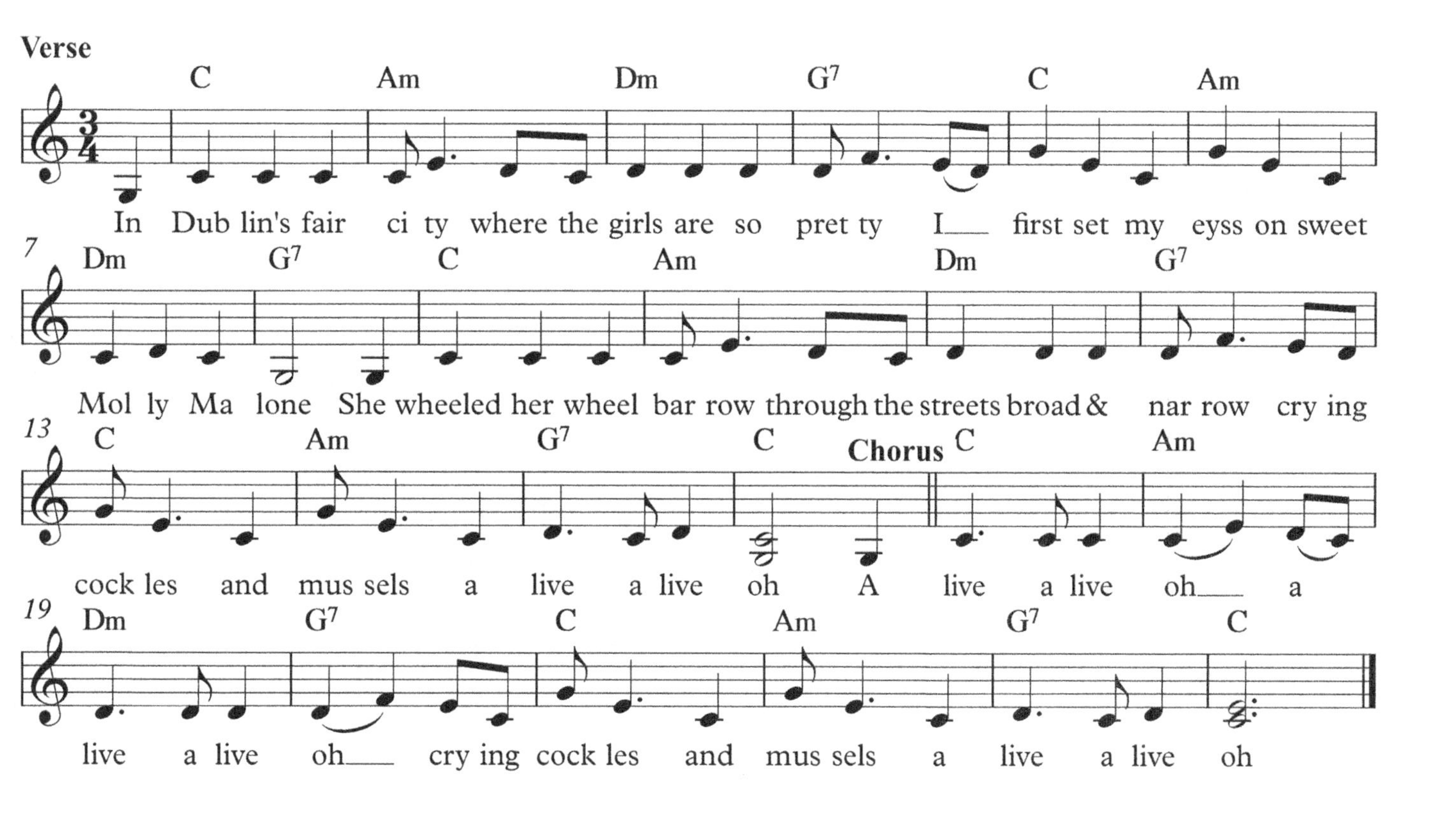

C Am
She was a fishmonger
Dm G7
And sure, twas no wonder
C Am Dm G7
For so were her mother and father before
C Am
And they wheeled their barrow
Dm G7
Through the streets broad and narrow
C Am G7 C
Crying "cockles and mussels, alive, alive, oh"
Chorus

C Am
She died of a fever
Dm G7
And sure, so one could save her
C Am Dm G7
And that was the end of sweet Molly Malone
C Am
Now her ghost wheels her barrow
Dm G7
Through the streets broad and narrow
C Am G7 C
Crying "cockles and mussels, alive, alive, oh"
Chorus

My Old Kentucky Home

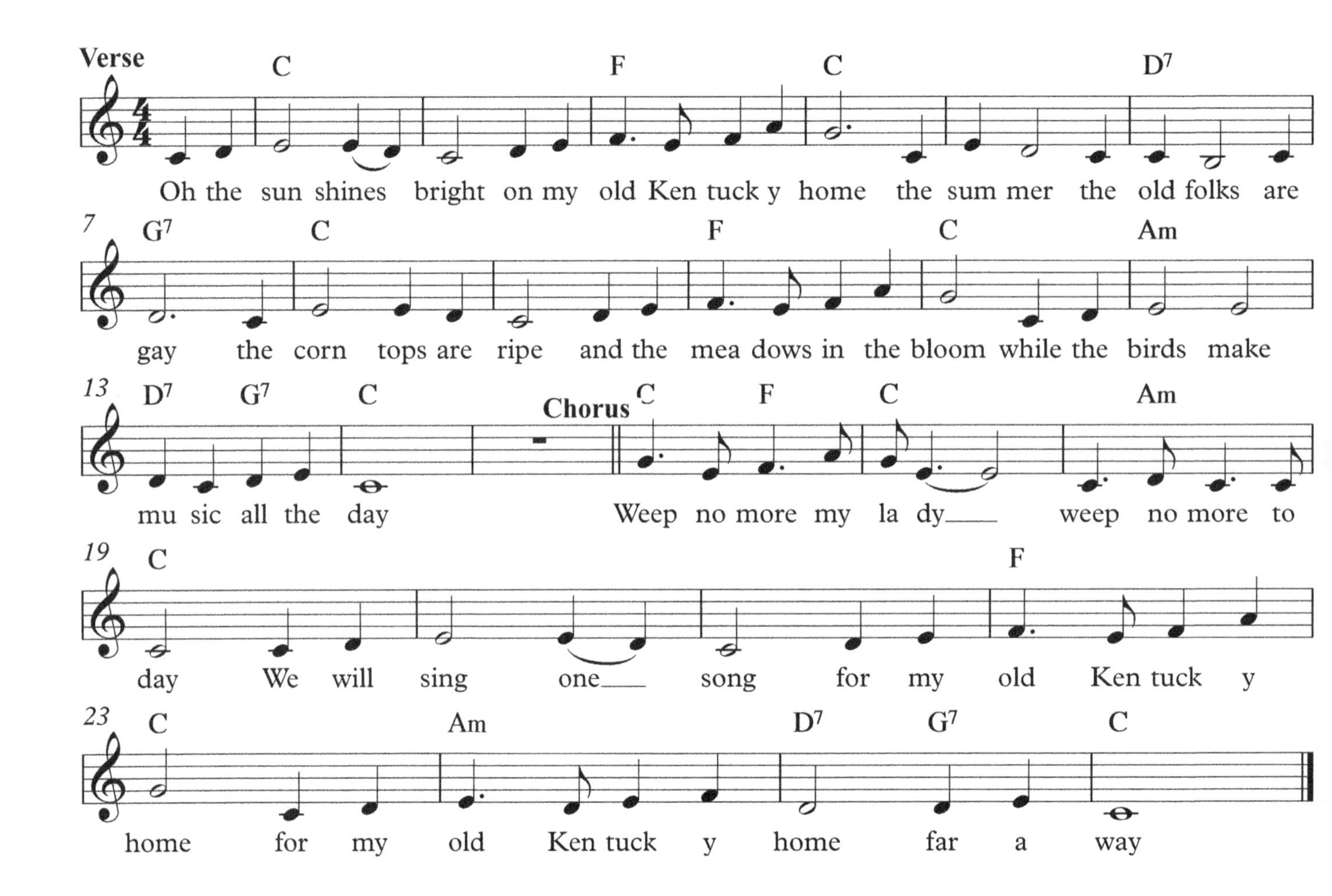

Well the young folks roll all around the cabin floor
They're merry, all happy and bright
By-and-by hard times will come a-knocking at my door
Then my old Kentucky home, goodnight
Chorus

Old Folks at Home

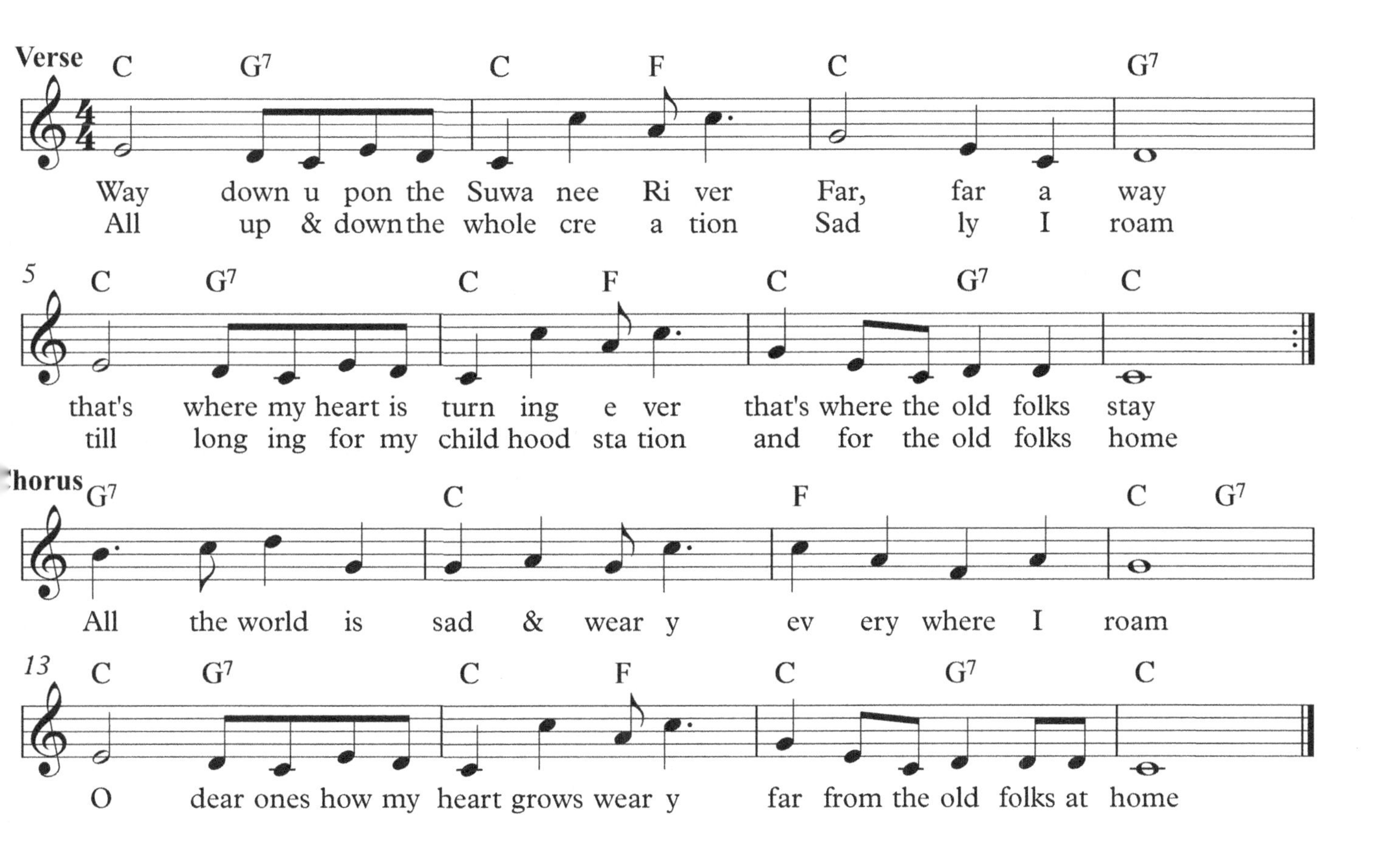

C G7 C F
All 'round the little farm I wandered
C G7
When I was young
C G7 C F
Then many happy days I squandered
C G7 C
Many the songs I sung
C G7 C F
When I was playing with my brother
C G7
Happy was I
C G7 C F
Oh, take me to my kind old mother
C G7 C
There let me live and die

Simple Gifts

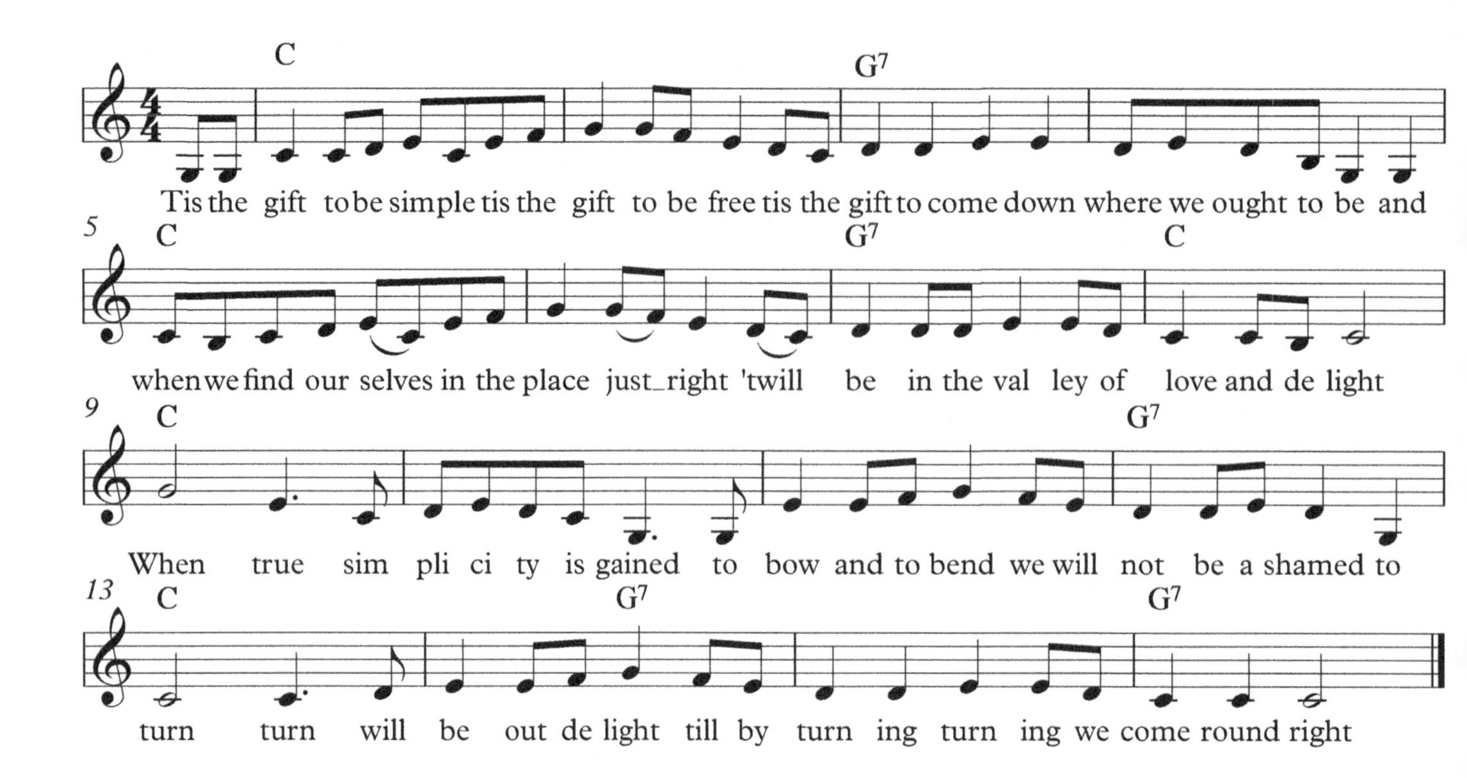

This is a one verse song. There are no additional lyrics.

Shenandoah

C
Shenandoah, I love your daughter
F C
Away, you rolling river
F C
I'll take her across the water
Am Em
Away, we're bound away,
C G7 C
Cross the wide Missouri

C
Seven years, I've been a rover
F C
Away, you rolling river
F C
Seven years I've been a rover
Am Em
Away, bound away,
C G7 C
Cross the wide Missouri

St. James Infirmary

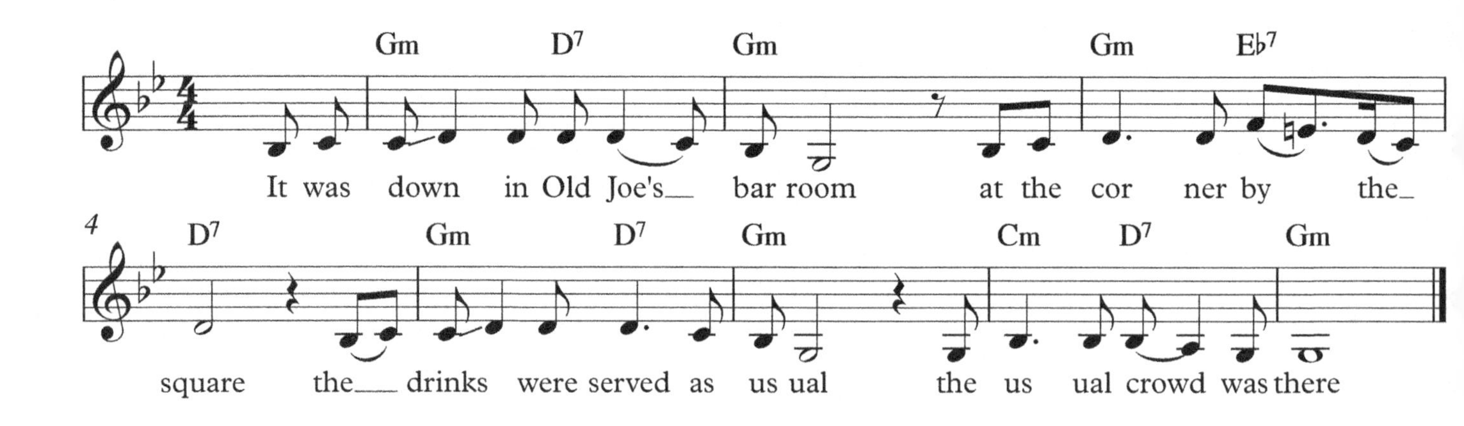

On my left stood Big Joe McKennedy
And his eyes were bloodshot red
And he turned his face to the people
These were the very words he said

I was down to St. James infirmary
I saw my baby there
She was stretched out on a long white table,
So sweet, cool and so fair

Let her go, let her go, God bless her
Wherever she may be
She may search this whole wide world over
Never find a sweeter man as me

When I die please bury me
In my high top Stetson hat
Put a twenty dollar gold piece on my watch chain
The gang'll know I died standing pat

Sweet Betsy From Pike

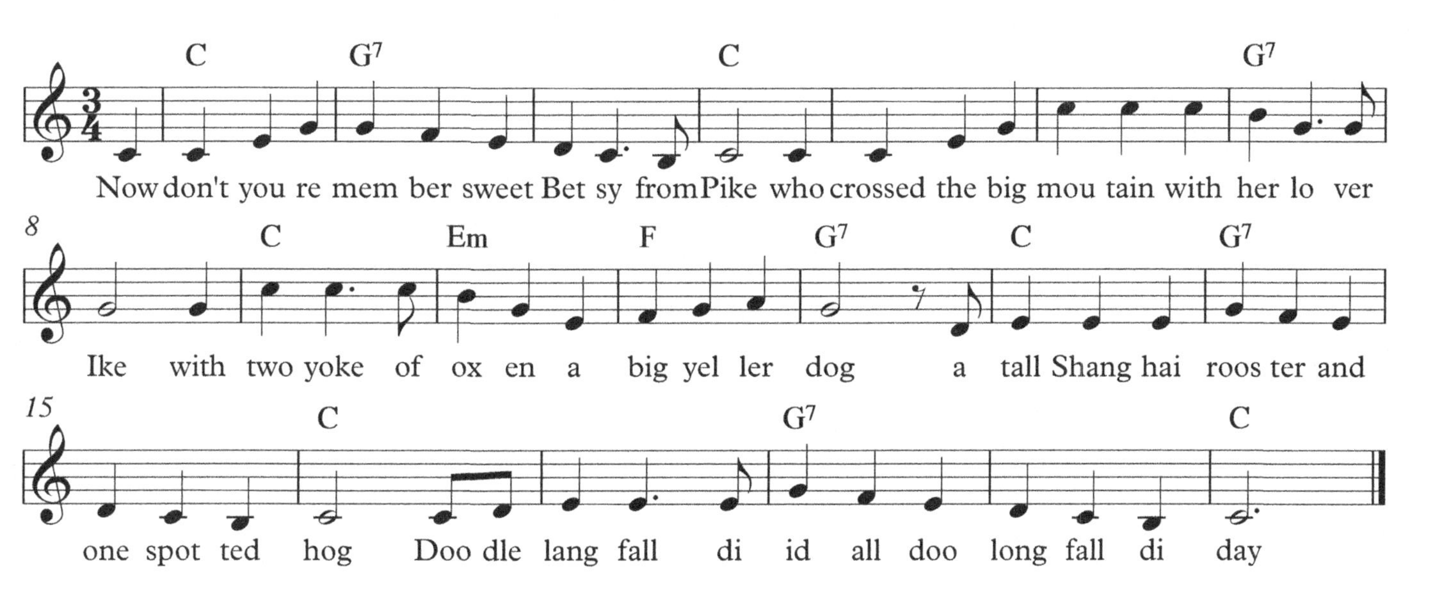

C G7 C
One evenin' quite early they camped on the plat
C G7
Down by the road on a green shady flat
C Em F G7
Where Betsy got tired and lay down to repose
C G7 C
And Ike he just gazed on his Pike County rose

C G7 C
Well they soon reached the desert where Betsy gave out
C G7
Down in the sand she lay rollin' about
C Em F G7
While Ike in great tears looked on in surprise
C G7 C
He said, "Betsy get up, you'll get sand in your eyes"

C G7 C
Well the Shanghai ran off and the cattle all died
C G7
The last piece of bacon that mornin' was fried
C Em F G7
Ike he got discouraged and Betsy got mad
C G7 C
The dog wagged his tail and looked wonderfully sad

C G7 C
Ike and sweet Betsy got married of course
C G7
But Ike gettin' jealous obtained the divorce
C Em F G7
Betsy well satisfied said with a shout
C G7 C
"Goodbye you big lummox, I'm glad you backed out"

Wreck of the Old 97

He turned and he said to his tired, greasy fireman,
"Shovel in a little more coal
And when we cross the White Oak Mountain
Just watch old 97 roll".

It's a mighty rough road from Lynchburg to Danville
A line on a three mile grade
It was on this grade that he lost his leverage
You can see what a jump he made

He was going down the grade making ninety miles an hour
When his whistle broke into a scream
He was found in the wreck with his hand on the throttle
Scalded to death by the steam

Now all you ladies, please take warning
From this time now and learn
Never speak harsh words to your true living husband
He may leave and never return

You Are My Sunshine

The other night dear, as I lay sleeping
I dreamed I held you in my arms
But when I awoke, dear, I was mistaken
So I hung my head and I cried
Chorus

I'll always love you and make you happy
If you will only say the same
But if you leave me and love another
You'll regret it all some day
Chorus

You told me once, dear, you really loved me
And no one else could come between
But now you've left me and love another
You have shattered all of my dreams
Chorus

Made in the USA
Coppell, TX
09 December 2022